SUNDAY EXPRESS & DAILY EXPRESS CARTOONS

FORTY NINTH SERIES

Giles Characters™ & © 1995 Express Newspapers plc.
Published by

BOOKS

The Old Rectory, Matford Lane, Exeter, Devon, EX2 4PS.
Under licence from Express Newspapers plc.
Printed in Italy. ISBN 1.874507-49-X

£4.99

GI 49

INTRODUCTION

by

LESLEY
JOSEPH
Actress

We have a long standing tradition in our house at Christmas that has gone on for as long as I remember. I always get bubble bath – my mother gets perfume – but my brother, oh joy, gets the Giles Annual, and promptly disappears for an hour, chortling and guffawing, while we wait patiently for him to finish it, so we can catch up with our favourite family.

Why do we love Giles so much – is it because he makes us laugh, or is it that we feel that his family is also our family? We know them all so well – they are so familiar to us, and yet so very much his own creation.

His cartoons seem to epitomise everything we love about this country, and no matter how much you look at them, you will always find something you missed – a child with his head in a bucket – glorious grandma swigging alcohol in a corner, even the animals have their own wicked personalities. This version of our little corner of the world is so special that you feel as long as Giles is around to stop us taking ourselves too seriously, life can't be too bad.

Thank you Giles for all the fun you bring to us – never change!

Lesly Joseph.

GILES COVER COLLECTION
Some outstanding examples from previous years' Annuals.

Annual 17. Published 1963.

GILES

Annual 30. Published 1976.

"It's somewhere different all right – and it's the last time Grandma arranges the bookings."

Daily Express, January 2nd, 1965

"That would be from the bride and bridegroom you booked yesterday, Jack."

Daily Express, February 2nd, 1965

"On the other hand, there's nothing in the rules to say skis <u>can't</u> be worn."

Daily Express, March 2nd, 1965

"'Heil! Britischer Schweinehunds!' didn't sound very matey."

Daily Express, May 20th, 1965

Postcard from Giles junior...

"I suppose you know they haven't actually got their pay increase yet?"

Daily Express, January 30th, 1966

"Good idea of yours for me to wear this for
protection against stink bombs —
unfortunately one's just got inside."

Daily Express, March 24th, 1966

"Nothing much – just that I don't think they thought a lot of
you calling them a two-timing, black-legging bunch of baskets."

Daily Express, May 17th, 1966

"It is kind of you to let us take a movie of our very own M.P. on holiday."

Daily Express, August 16th, 1966

"On guard! Harry the Ulcer's just taken me for three weeks of my pay rise."

Sunday Express, September 4th, 1966

"Madam, I assure you there's no danger of my company folding and your 7d.
a week for the last sixty years going up the spout."

Daily Express, January 23rd, 1967

"He's got a point. If the secret documents he found belong to the
Minister, what the hell was the Minister doing playing on his swing?"

Daily Express, March 14th, 1967

"'Tis but a teenage jest, thou sayest? By the Bard, it had better be says I."

Daily Express, April 18th, 1967

"While you're at it, put 'Many Happy Returns, Hitler.' It's his birthday today."

Daily Express, April 20th, 1967

"Serg. – Chief Inspector Boggis from the Yard, who you called in to investigate the deficit in our petty cash."

Daily Express, August 3rd, 1967

"On your feet, Sir Francis – we've won ten years' free mooring in the Daily Express Boat Show competition."

Daily Express, January 2nd, 1968

"Dad says can we have one bottle for Tibby and two bottles for my hamster?"

Sunday Express, August 18th, 1968

"Never mind about Him Chief want 25% cut of the profits —
we want Him Chief to hand back the Lord Mayor right now."

Daily Express, September 24th, 1968

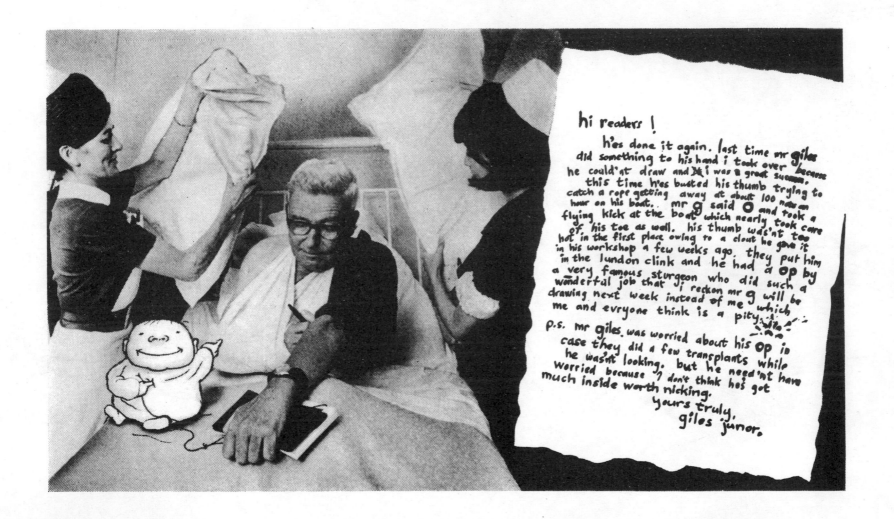

Sunday Express, September 29th, 1968

"It'll either put an end to their cold war or start another with Moscow and the States."

Daily Express, November 7th, 1968

"Hold it, lads – it's the Chief Constable. Sorry Sir, we thought it was a courting couple."

Daily Express, November 19th, 1968

"I didn't know the darned thing was loaded."

Daily Express, February 25th, 1969

"They must have given us the slip between the Arsenal ground and here."

Sunday Express, March 30th, 1969

"This lot won't fetch much on the hijack exchange market, Gonzales."

Sunday Express, September 7th, 1969

"Henry!"

Sunday Express, October 5th, 1969

"Well <u>somebody</u> phoned from this address to ask us to collect a corpse."

Daily Express, April 7th, 1970

"Thank Tony Jacklin for the course crawling with golf-mad truants."

Daily Express, June 25th, 1970

"Me thinks 'tis not a freak summer storm that causeth rain to gush forth from the wings."

Sunday Express, August 9th, 1970

"I don't think the Aussies quite liked the idea of being disqualified."

Daily Express, September 24th, 1970

"Santa received your letter, Basher."

Daily Express, December 24th, 1970

"Hold tight, sir."

Daily Express, March 30th, 1971

"No, no, mummy – it wasn't the Ref who pushed me, it was this one over here."

Sunday Express, August 22nd, 1971

"Calling all ham-radio operators, are you sitting comfortably? Then we'll begin. At present we are doing the Baker Street police canteen till..."

Daily Express, September 14th, 1971

"In every Grandma's handbag there is a Russian field-marshal's two-way radio and a do-it-yourself micro-film outfit."

"This suspicious note you saw dropped, Sir. After exhaustive investigations by MI5 and our forensic experts it turned out to be a fruit-gum wrapper."

Sunday Express, October 3rd, 1971

"Know what we forgot?"

Sunday Express, October 10th, 1971

"You've got a job *where*?"

Daily Express, January 20th, 1972

"Attention everybody — new cause for tears. Billy Smart's Circus coming off the road."

Sunday Express, February 6th, 1972

"Romeo, Romeo, wherefore art thou Romeo?"

Daily Express, June 13th, 1972

"Resist, man — remember if we don't get a job we might have to come back after the hols."

Daily Express, July 20th, 1972

"I only asked her if now that Boots are printing nude holiday snaps she'd mind taking her hat off."

Daily Express, August 24th, 1972

"Dinger, we learn from the grapevine that your Teddy Bear
mascot contains four knuckle-dusters, two files and a hacksaw."

Daily Express, August 29th, 1972

"She makes a better Hitler than Alec Guinness even without a moustache."

Daily Express, May 12th, 1973

"Pity, now we'll have to think of something else for your brother's wedding present."

Daily Express, July 14th, 1973

a hoy,

there me heartys,

in the blessed event of

mr **giles** taking a short holday here we

are again standing in for him in loo of.

although **mr g** is always in and out of

other poeples' countries he never takes a holday as

he hates them.   the last time he took a holday

was while he was having **his** pnewmonia and it

was nice and quiet around the house.

mrs **giles** don't like him taking holdays

CONTD. →

because he's ~~an even more miserable~~

even more niggly when he comes

back than before he went.   anyway she don't

call this one a holday because he's on his

littel new boats and 'she hates boats new or old.

yours faithfully until next

week, **giles junor.**

<u>ps</u> we all laughed just now when we heard the shipping

forecasts which said it was blowing ~~like~~ force 8

and don't look very good for weeks and mr g is stuck out

in the north sea somewhere nice and cold.

<u>pps</u> mrs g says he's more likely doing a pub crawl

round the british isles.

A hoy there again me heartys,

just a few lines to let you know that **mr giles** is still mallingring on his littel boat and gawd help evrybody next week when he has to go back to work to earn pennys to buy us all buppy. he used some funny littel words when grandma suddenly bawled out "a hoy!" land a head! and **mr g** said so there ~~xxxx~~ should be considering we've been anchored outside the clubhouse for the last 3 days. i don't think he's enjoying his holday very much especially when he heard that lord beaverbrooks shares have gone up while he's away instead of taking a dive ah well i must close now rule brittania and all that

yours truly,

giles junor

PS. talking of brittania **mr g** says he can't wait to see what littel old **johnny gordon** has to say about the royal yot having a £1¾ million refit for cows week for cows week ho ho.

PPS. **mrs g** says if the **queen's** boatyard bills are anything like **mr g's** she won't see a fat lot for £1¾m.

PPPS. **mr g** has called his new boat "CIRCE" after the greek enchantress who used to turn all sailors into swine and he don't know anything that can do that quicker than a boat.

PPPPS. he says he likes being stuck in the middle of the ocean because it's the one place certain littel copper hasnt stuck a parking ticket on him. yet. xx

Sunday Express, August 5th, 1973

"That wasn't a very nice thing to say, Grandma – 'About the weight of his head.'"

Daily Express, September 11th, 1973

"Anything to declare Madam?"

Sunday Express, September 30th, 1973

"You're good boys to think of paper saving, but I don't think daddy will like you cutting up his paper before he's read it."

Daily Express, January 22nd, 1974

"Lady, you don't happen to have one about horses being unfair to riders?"

Daily Express, April 30th, 1974

"Hell, Mary-Jo, it IS July the Fourth."

Daily Express, July 4th, 1974

"By gad, Madam! You've called out my private National Emergency Army to rescue your damn Tibby!"

Sunday Express, August 25th, 1974

"Twas in Windsor Park. She came at me with the old Kung-Fu — locked me with a half Nelson, I gazed into her eyes and swooned, your Honour."

Daily Express, August 31st, 1974

"I would advise Class to forget these stories in the papers about bottom-spanking being fun."

Daily Express, November 21st, 1974

"Can't tell the difference between the taste of hijackers and Chief Stewards!"

Daily Express, January 9th, 1975

"You're well over the maximum **68** degrees, old boy."

Daily Express, January 14th, 1975

"Typical constructive summing up of the Tory dilemma – if she was Ted she'd shove off on a boat and let 'em al! stew."

Daily Express, February 7th, 1975

"Our Head Lad heard papa say if he has his way he'd black his other eye."

Sunday Express, May 4th, 1975

"Remind me to have a word with Edward about his girl friends phoning the Palace at two in the morning."

Daily Express, January 13th, 1976

"That's another thing we've got to thank their generation for."

Daily Express, January 27th, 1976

"I've had an exhausting day at the office dear ... by the way, have the children been behaving themselves?"

Daily Express, June 8th, 1976

"Grandma! Come indoors at once!"

Sunday Express, June 27th, 1976

"Mine's not a Prime Minister but the thought has crossed my mind."

Sunday Express, March 13th, 1977

Daily Express, November 21st, 1977

"It ain't my fault fares are going up again — so cut out the Colonel Bogey."

Daily Express, December 5th, 1977

"Would you please tell Mr. MacTavish that Burns' birthday celebrations do not start until after office hours."

Daily Express, January 25th, 1978

"When you get fed-up roaming the streets of Ilford, make sure you don't call a cab driver with a name like Rosenbloom, son."

Daily Express, February 24th, 1978

"Industrial Tribunal? We're surrounded by a mob of unreasonable commuters
and we've run out of tea-bags – what are you going to do about it?"

Daily Express, August 10th, 1978

"It says: 'Thanks for the publicity, girls,' and signed: 'Sexy Fiona'."

Daily Express, February 22nd, 1979

"You'll spoil their Mother's Day if you're going to sit there muttering: 'They charged them £6.50 for that?'"

Sunday Express, March 25th, 1979

"They gave the Queen a small bouquet for it."

Daily Express, May 31st, 1979

"Hear that, everybody? If some of you don't start enjoying yourselves Father won't bring us again next year."

Sunday Express, August 26th, 1979

Daily Express, January 3rd, 1980

"Vera thinks she's helping the BBC save its £130 million by not switching it on."

Sunday Express, March 2nd, 1980

"We had a super weekend in Scarborough — my hero belted a woman copper and kicked down 37 kiddies' sand castles."

Daily Express, April 8th, 1980

"Football all day yesterday – non-stop cricket today – he'll tire himself out for his Day of Action on Wednesday."

Sunday Express, May 11th, 1980

Whatever happened to old-fashioned romance?

FROM YESTERDAY'S DAILY EXPRESS

"No dear, Anna Ford's lucky – she can't see daddy at breakfast time."

Daily Express, December 30th, 1980

"I'm sure it was nothing to do with your dog's colour – Butch bit him because he caught him in his basket."

Daily Express, April 16th, 1981

"Couldn't you just wear it down to the Club to please them?"

Sunday Express, June 21st, 1981

"Hold tight on the BBC whoever axed her Kenneth Kendall!"

Daily Express, June 30th, 1981

"Go tell mummy Geoffrey Howe says the recession's over, so you can buy two each."

Daily Express, August 4th, 1981

"Look what he's done on me 'at!"

Daily Express, October 1st, 1981

"Grandma won't be very happy when she finds you've eaten her £1 million Express Bingo book."

Daily Express, October 8th, 1981

"Cover me while I see what that boy's up to – he could have been reading subversive literature."

Daily Express, February 25th, 1982

"Vera, I think you've been doing a bit too much of this Daily Express F-slimming plan!"

Daily Express, May 18th, 1982

"If my great-grandfather sold your great-great-grandfather to Argentina, in effect, you've been supplying the enemy with fresh beef for the duration."

Daily Express, June 3rd, 1982

"Her Majesty appreciates your desire to ensure maximum security ... now hop off."

Daily Express, July 13th, 1982

"I suppose one might say I'm unique – I've never been married to Richard Burton."

Daily Express, July 7th, 1983

"Listen Mac – my birthday's the same day as the Queen Mum's and I'm not leaving here until she arrives."

Daily Express, August 4th, 1983

"You're the sort that gets the rest of us a bad name – coming last in every race!"

Daily Express, August 11th, 1983

"Considering what they cost a packet, 60 million is not all that much."

Daily Express, September 15th, 1983

"Your elephant-trap to catch Russell Harty is working, Grandma —
we've got the milkman, the baker, Mrs Mainwaring's labrador..."

Daily Express, September 20th, 1983

"What an extraordinary thing to tell us to do with our empty tea cups."

Daily Express, October 20th, 1983

"None of 'em will ever learn – I got six across the backside for writing 'Peace' on the school wall when I were a boy."

Daily Express, November 15th, 1983

"It was perhaps indiscreet to call her a heathen because she says she's going to watch the new TV series about Jesus."

Sunday Express, April 8th, 1984

"I'm trying to imagine a cane and black-stockinged suspender service around here."

Daily Express, June 26th, 1984

"If your licence does go up to £10, in future the slippers will be delivered right here."

Sunday Express, July 8th, 1984

"Somebody is breaking the new law already. I can smell smoke."

Daily Express, July 10th, 1984

"Would the Dennis Taylor who filled these triangles with snooker balls kindly step forward."

Daily Express, October 30th, 1984